Moral Stories

Happy Monk

& Other Stories

Published by

MAPLE PRESS PRIVATE LIMITED
office: A-63, Sector 58, Noida 201301, U.P., India
phone: +91 120 455 3581, 455 3583
email: info@maplepress.co.in
website: www.maplepress.co.in

Reprinted in 2019
Printed and bound in Noida, India

ISBN: 978-93-50335-26-0

Happy Monk

Long ago, there lived a very rich man. As he became older he realised that both the rich and the poor suffered equally when they were old. Enlightened, he left behind his luxurious life and traveled to the forest where he would meditate all the time until he gained wisdom.

Because the old monk was so friendly and wise, he gained over five hundred followers who began living with him in the forest.

Though monks were meant to look serious, one of them would always wear a slight smile on his face. No matter what happened, he never lost this glimmer of inner happiness. Everybody would ask him about what made him so happy but he would chuckle and say, "If I told you, you wouldn't believe me. And if you thought I spoke a lie, it would dishonor my master."

But the wise old master knew of his secret. He knew that the smile would never be wiped from the monk's face. Thus the happy monk was his number one assistant.

One spring, the monks decided to go to the city. The king was a kind and a generous man. He welcomed the monks and offered them to stay at the pleasure garden.

This great king took his responsibilities as a ruler very seriously. But he was always worried. He worried about the neighbouring kingdoms which were hostile and constantly threatened the peace of his kingdom. He had to often make peace between his own ministers.

Sometimes his wives fought for his attention and his sons fought amongst themselves for the throne. Sometimes, a dissatisfied subject would threaten his life and he constantly worried about the finances of his kingdom. The king was not happy. He never had the time to be happy.

The monks enjoyed their stay but when it was time for them to go back to the forest, the king approached the master and said, "Your reverence, if your disciples wish to go back, they are most welcome. But you are old and weak. What will you go back to the forest for? Please remain in the garden of pleasure and allow us the opportunity to serve you."

So the master called the happy monk and asked him to lead the others into the forest as their new master.

The happy monk as asked by his master took the remaining disciples to the forest. There he gained more wisdom by meditating and his inner happiness increased by folds.

One day, he came back to meet his master. He sat down at his master's feet and for a very long time, they did not speak to each other.

When the king came to pay a visit he was astonished at the smile on the happy monk's face. He asked the master, "Your reverence, how is it that he smiles so much? Does nothing in the world worry him?"

"You wouldn't believe if I told you," said the master. "He was once a king, same as you. Just as mighty, just as fair. But he realised that true happiness lies neither in power nor in wealth. True happiness lies in freedom from it. He left all that behind and since then, that smile has not left his face."

The happy monk got up to leave, as the king bowed to him with respect.

Moral : Happiness seeks those who do not seek wealth or power.

United We Stand

Long ago, in a certain village lived a hardworking farmer. He had a small piece of land and he worked on it day and night to make a living. His only sorrow was his five sons. His sons were very lazy. Instead of helping their father they spent their days idling and quarreling amongst themselves.

When the farmer grew old, he began to worry. "My sons keep fighting amongst themselves. When I am dead, they will divide the tiny bit of land I have. Then it will not be sufficient for any one of them. Also, people might want to take advantage of their quarrels. I must do something to teach them a lesson," he thought.

The clever farmer gathered some sticks. He tied the sticks into a bundle and called his sons. He then handed the bundle to them and asked them to take turns and try to break the bundle. They tried their best but even the strongest of the brothers could not snap the bundle. One of them suggested, "Father, untie the bundle and give it to

us. It will be much easier to break the bundle that way."

"Exactly!" said their father. "If each of you chooses to live by yourself, other people will try to take advantage of you. But if you choose to stay together, then no one can harm you."

The brothers understood their father's advice. They decided to stop quarreling and start living together in harmony.

Moral : United we stand. Divided we fall.

The Woodcutter and His Foolish Son

In a small village near the dense forest lived a woodcutter with his wife and son. The woodcutter was a very hard working fellow. Every day at dawn, he would leave his house to chop wood in the forest and not return until it was dark.

His son was slow-witted. The woodcutter realised that he was too foolish to be able to learn any other trade. So he took his son with him every day to teach him how to chop wood.

One day, the woodcutter's wife asked the son to carry some rice and curry to his father in the woods. When the son reached, it was time for lunch and the woodcutter was hungry. They sat down in the shade of a tree and ate the rice and curry. Then the woodcutter asked his son to chop some wood to carry home. The son picked up the spare axe and got down to work.

They were working when suddenly a wasp flew from

the bushes nearby and began distracting them. The woodcutter waved his hands in irritation. Then he waved the towel that hung around his shoulders. But the wasp did not leave. It kept on buzzing around them

The woodcutter said to his son, "Can you kill this wasp? It is bothering me." The son who was chopping a large branch waved his hands at the wasp. He then waved a leafy stick at it. But the wasp continued buzzing.

It flew and sat on the woodcutter's shoulder. The son had an idea. With a large block of wood, he hit the woodcutter's shoulder. His father howled in pain. The wasp was killed but the woodcutter was hurt very badly. It was a long time before he was well again.

Moral : Never trust a fool.

The Ant and The Pigeon

Once upon a time, beside a mighty river stood a large, leafy Mango tree. Many pigeons made their nests in that Mango tree. They lived there happily as the tree would give them sweet fruits to eat.

During the summer, the tree would be drooping with mangoes. The pigeons would then have a feast every day.

Under that same tree there was a large ant hill. Thousands of ants lived in that ant hill. During the summers, they too would feast on the fallen mangoes. Life could not get better for them.

One day, a pigeon was looking out at the river from its nest in the tree. Suddenly it noticed that an ant had fallen into the river and was drowning. The ant was trying its best to swim and reach the bank but the current was too strong for it. But the brave ant kept on fighting for its life.

The pigeon was moved. It took pity on the tiny ant. With its beak, it tore a leaf from the nearest branch and flew to the river. Then it threw the leaf into the river.

The ant hurried and climbed on the leaf that was now floating. The leaf drifted ashore with the current and the ant was saved.

The ant could never forget what the pigeon had done for him that day. He began to look for an opportunity to return the favour. And the day soon arrived.

A hunter had found out that many pigeon lived in the mango tree. The ant was carrying some food back to the ant hill when it saw the hunter aiming at the tree with him bow and arrow. The ant was frightened. It turned towards the tree and saw that the hunter was aiming at the pigeon which had saved his life. It was his turn now.

Quietly he climbed up the hunter's leg and walked through his body to his head. As the hunter was about to let go of the arrow, it stung the hunter in the corner of his eye. The sting was sharp and it distracted the hunter. The hunter groaned with pain. His groan was so loud that it echoed through the fields and made the pigeons in the mango tree fly away as they sensed the danger.

The pigeon was saved. Though it never found out how the ant had saved its life, but the ant felt very happy for the pigeon.

Moral : If you do good deeds, good things will happen to you.

The Hat Seller and The Monkeys

Once upon a time, there was a man who sold hats to make a living. He would carry colourful hats in a large bundle and would walk from town to town, selling them. The children loved him for he was amusing as he himself wore a colourful hat on his head. Over time he had gained many customers for his hats.

One day as he was walking from one town to another, he spotted a large banyan tree. The hat seller was tired. It was noon and he had been walking all day, selling hats. He decided to rest under the banyan tree.

He set the bundle at the foot of the banyan tree and lay down for a nap. Suddenly he was woken by a loud chatter. On that banyan tree lived a troop of monkeys. When the monkeys saw the bundle, they were curious to know what was inside it. The mischievous monkeys had each taken a hat from the bundle and were now wearing them on their heads.

The hat seller was puzzled to find all his hats gone. When he looked around, he saw that the monkeys were wearing them. He was in deep trouble. He thought, "Stupid monkeys. What do I do now? I can chase them with a stick. But that won't bring the hats back to me."

He stood there and scratched his head. Suddenly he noticed that the monkeys were scratching their heads too.

He pulled a face at the monkeys. The monkeys too pulled faces at him. He then slammed his forehead. All the monkeys slammed their foreheads. He realised what was happening.

The smart hat seller then took off his hat and threw it on the ground. The monkeys followed him and threw their hats on the ground too. He was waiting for this. He quickly collected the hats and put them back in his bundle.

The monkeys looked on as the hat seller walked away from the tree, humming to himself.

Moral : Be wise and you will find your way.

When Mr. Crow Got Tricked

You have read how clever Mr. Crow managed to drink the water that was beyond his reach. But sometimes, even clever people get tricked. Here is what happened once that left Mr. Crow totally bewildered.

Once upon a time, Mr. Crow was circling a garbage dump. Suddenly he spotted a big juicy bone. Mr. Crow was overjoyed. He had been feeding on dry orange peels for a long time. "What a treat!" he thought. "I must grab it before anybody else sees it."

Thinking thus he picked the bone in his beak and flew to perch on a roof. Suddenly a fox approached him. The fox too had been looking for something to eat. It noticed the juicy bone in Mr. Crow's beak. The cunning fox had a plan to get the bone.

It went to the roof where Mr. Crow was sitting and said, "Hello there friend. Perhaps you do not know me but I happen to be a friend of your friend, Mr. Kite. He

told me, what a lovely voice you have. He told me that you had sung a fabulous song, on his birthday. Today is my birthday. Will you be kind and sing me a song too?"

The Crow thought, "Wow! He is praising me. I must oblige this good fox and sing him a song." And Mr. Crow cocked his head and flapped his wings and sang loudly. Just as he had done that the bone fell from his beak and landed straight in front of the fox. The fox was waiting. He picked up the bone and ran towards the forest.

Moral : Never believe the one who flatters you.

The Blue Jackal

In a forest near a village lived a jackal. Although he was a timid fellow, he was also very greedy. One day the jackal went into the village to steal some hens. When he entered a coop, the hens began to make a lot of noise. Hearing the noise some people came out with axes in their hands and their dogs by their side and began chasing the jackal.

The jackal was in a fix. The forest was far and he knew he would not be able to outrun the men and their dogs.

He saw an empty drum behind one of the shops. The jackal quickly climbed onto the drum and hid inside it until the trouble passed. When the neighbourhood was quiet again, the jackal crept out of the drum and walked into the forest.

All that running had made him thirsty. The jackal walked to a river for a drink of water. Suddenly he noticed that he no longer looked the way he used to. He had turned blue all over.

The drum that he was hiding in had belonged to a dye shop. The owner had stored blue dye in it. When the jackal hid in the drum his coat got blue dye on it. The jackal was amazed at his new look. An idea struck him. "What if I am able to fool all these stupid animals of the forest? I would never have to risk my neck to steal a hen again."

He proudly strutted into the forest and called a meeting. He declared, "Listen everyone. As you must have guessed it already by now, I am the only one of my kind. I was sent by God to rule over all other animals. From today, you will respect me, care for me and bring me food if you fear for the safety of the forest and your lives."

All the animals were scared. They bowed to the blue jackal in respect. Life for the jackal improved. He would sit under a large tree and eat and roll in the dirt all day. The other animals would bring him food and care for his needs. He began to grow fat.

But some of the jackals were not convinced that he was sent by God. They suspected him to be a jackal like themselves. So they held a meeting among themselves and decided, "Tonight at midnight when the whole forest would be sleeping, we would join our voices together and howl. Let's see if our king howls with us, for if he does, we will know he is nothing but a jackal who is trying to fool us."

So at midnight the jackals joined their voices and howled loudly. The blue jackal who was fast asleep, woke up with the sound. And because he was indeed a jackal he could not help but howl at the top of his voice on hearing the others.

Soon he was caught and was chased out of the forest by all the other animals whom he had tried to fool.

Moral : One must never lie.

The Crows and The Cobra

Long ago in a kingdom, beside the royal ghats, stood a large tree. A father crow and a mother crow had built their nest in one of its branches. When it was spring, the mother crow laid some eggs which hatched into beautiful chicks with time. The father crow and the mother crow were very happy and proud of the chicks.

At the foot of that tree was a hole where lived a black cobra snake. The snake was very cunning. All through spring he would sit listening to the chicks in the nest and think of eating them up one day. And that day came. When both the father crow and the mother crow were away, the snake quietly climbed the tree and reached the nest. The chicks were waiting for their parents in the nest.

The snake thought, "It is my lucky day!" and he gobbled all the chicks one by one.

When the father crow and the mother crow returned they were shocked to find the cage empty. The mother

crow began to cry, "O my poor children. What could have happened to you? Who could have visited our nest while we were away?" The father crow tried to calm her, "Don't worry dear. Whoever has done it, his deed will not go unpunished."

The next day the mother crow went to find food. But the father crow stayed back hidden behind the leaves. It was then he noticed the fat black cobra. The father crow instantly knew that it could only have been the cobra which had eaten his chicks. He knew he would not be able to fight the cobra as it was very poisonous and dangerous.

He began to think of a plan. He saw that just then the prince had come to the ghat for a dip in the cool water. He had taken off his clothes and his gold chain and was now swimming in the water with pleasure.

An idea struck the crow. He swooped down and picked up the gold chain when the attendant was not looking and threw the chain down the snake's hole. When the prince started to dress again, he couldn't find the chain. Several men were called from the royal palace to look for the chain.

They looked in every bush and turned every stone. Finally they found something gleaming in a hole under the tree. When they went to pull the chain out of the hole they saw the snake resting in there. They soon killed the snake, took the chain and went back to the palace.

When the mother crow came back in the evening, the father crow told her, "We are safe now. The evil snake is dead."

Moral : Intelligence is greater than physical power.